Phonics

I Hear Thunder

Published in the UK by Scholastic Education, 2022
Scholastic Distribution Centre, Bosworth Avenue, Tournament Fields, Warwick, CV34 6UQ
Scholastic Ireland, 89E Lagan Road, Dublin Industrial Estate, Glasnevin, Dublin, D11 HP5F

Printed by Ashford Colour Press
The book is made of materials from well-managed, FSC-certified forests
and other controlled sources.

A CIP catalogue record for this book is available from the British Library.

ISBN 978-0702-30899-4

Author
Becca Heddle
Editorial team
Rachel Morgan, Vicki Yates, Tracy Kewley, Jennie Clifford
Design team
Dipa Mistry, Justin Hoffmann, Andrea Lewis, We Are Grace
Illustrations
Veronica Chaves represented by Lemonade illustration agency

Help your child to read!

This book practises these letters and letter sounds.
Point and say the sounds with your child:

ar **ur** **ow** **ear** **er**

Your child may need help to read these common tricky words:

I **my** **the** **are** **you** **all** **me** **no** **and**

Before reading

- Look at the cover picture and read the title together. Read the back cover blurb to your child.
- Ask your child: *Have you noticed a thunderstorm at night? What was it like?*

During reading

- If your child gets stuck on a word, remind them to sound it out and then blend the sounds to read the word: h-ur-t, hurt.
- If they are still stuck, show them how to read the word.
- Enjoy looking at the pictures together. Pause to talk about the story.

After reading

- Ask your child: *Did the boy stay scared? Why not? Who do you feel safest with?*

Can you spot the
parrot on 6 pages?

I hear a sharp bang.
It is thunder.

Now the power is off.

It is too dark. I am upset.

I get down
under the bed.

It is my sister.

The lightning is sudden and harsh.

Retell the story

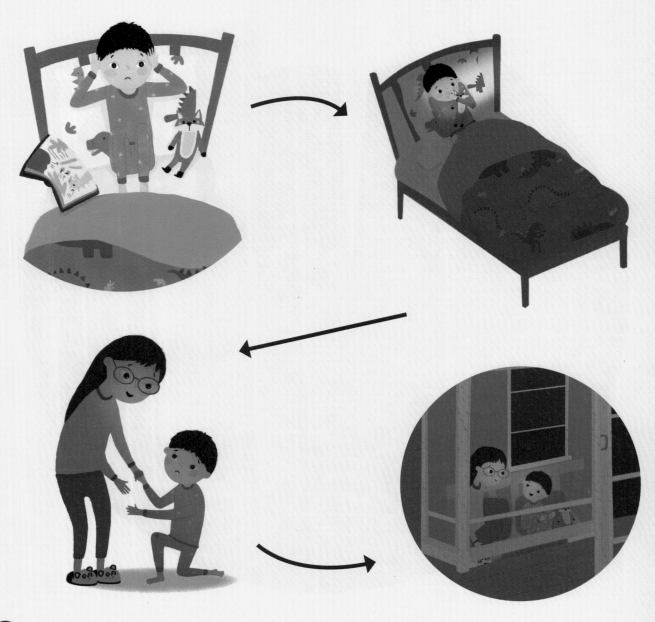